Chip was watching television. The magic
key was on the arm of the chair. Nadim
came to play.

Chip didn't want to play. He wanted to
watch television. He wanted to watch a
programme about magpies.

Nadim wanted a magic adventure. Chip looked for the magic key, but he couldn't find it. Nadim helped Chip to look.

Chip looked at the armchair.

"I put the key on the arm of the chair," he said.

Suddenly, he had an idea.

The children looked in the armchair.
They found lots of things. Chip found
Mum's missing ear-ring.

"Mum will be pleased," he said.

Chip found the key. It was stuck to a
toffee.

"Yuk!" said Chip. "It's all sticky."

Chip told Mum about the armchair. He gave Mum the missing ear-ring. Nadim cleaned the key. He made it very shiny.

The children went into Biff's room. Biff
looked at the key.

"Oh no! It looks very shiny," she said. "I
hope the magic still works."

Suddenly, the key began to glow. It looked very bright. The magic took the children into a new adventure.

The children were in a wood. Chip
didn't like it. The wood was dark and
gloomy.

"Come on!" he said.

Suddenly, Biff saw something shiny. She picked it up.

"What a beautiful ring!" she said. "Somebody must have dropped it."

The children saw some soldiers. The
soldiers saw the ring. They grabbed the
children.

"That ring is stolen," they said.

The soldiers took the children to the prince.

"We've found your thieves," they said. "Here's your ring."

"Here are the thieves," said the prince.
"What else have they stolen?"
    "My watch was stolen," said a man.
    "My ear-ring was stolen," said a lady.

A soldier took the magic key.

"Look at this shiny key," he said. "These children have stolen things. They must have locked them away."

The soldiers took the children to a prison.

"Where are the stolen things?" they asked. "Tell us, or we'll lock you up."

Suddenly, a magpie flew down. It took the magic key.

"Stop that magpie!" called Biff. "It's stolen the key."

The magpie flew to the woods.

"The magpie is the thief," said Chip.

The children ran after the magpie.

Everyone ran after the children.

The magpie flew to a tree.

"Look in its nest," said Chip.

Nadim climbed the tree.

"Be careful," called Biff.

Nadim looked in the magpie's nest. It
was full of shiny things. Nadim gasped.
"What beautiful things!" he said.

"You see!" said Anneena, crossly. "We
aren't thieves. The magpie took your
things."

"Sorry!" said the soldier.

Everyone was pleased.

"Here's my missing ear-ring," said a lady.

"Here's my watch," said a man.

The prince gave the children a medal.
"The magpie was the thief," he said.
"Sorry, we thought it was you."
The magic key began to glow.

"Magpies like shiny things," said Biff.
"So it was a good job Nadim made the
magic key shiny, after all."